This book belongs to

....

Quarto Knows

Quarto is the authority on a wide range of topics.

Quarto educates, entertains and enriches the lives of our readers—enthusiasts and lovers of hands-on living.

www.quartoknows.com

First published in 2018 by QED Publishing,
an imprint of The Quarto Group.
The Old Brewery, 6 Blundell Street,
London N7 9BH, United Kingdom.
T (0)20 7700 6700 F (0)20 7700 8066
www.QuartoKnows.com

A catalogue record for this book is available from the British Library.

ISBN 978-1-91241-379-9

Based on the original story by Bernard Ashley and Janee Trasler
Author of adapted text: Katie Woolley
Series Editor: Joyce Bentley
Series Designer: Sarah Peden

Manufactured in Dongguan, China TL042018

9 8 7 6 5 4 3 2 1

FSC
www.fsc.org

MIX
Paper from
responsible sources

FSC® C104723

Reading Gems

The Party Dress

Jed's mum and dad had been invited
to a party.

Mum wanted to buy
a new dress.

Let's go to
the shops!

Good
idea!

Dad worked at the car garage. Mum and Jed took Dad to work in the car.

Then they went into town.
Mum took Jed past the toyshop and into
the shop next door.

7

First, Mum put on a red and blue cowboy dress. It had lots of tassels!

Mum showed Jed.

I like it!

Jed wanted to be a cowboy one day.

Mum wanted to put on another dress.

Next, Mum put on a short black and white dress.

Jed thought Mum looked like a footballer.

I like it!

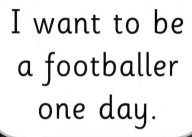

Mum shook her head and went to put on another outfit.

I like this yellow and blue dress better. It is like the sand and sea.

I like it!

Jed liked the sand and sea too.

But Mum wasn't sure so she put on a pirate outfit.

I like it!

I'm Pirate Annie!

Jed wanted to be a pirate one day too.

The last dress was a green one. Mum showed it to Jed and the shopkeeper.

I could dress up as Robin Hood!

I like it!

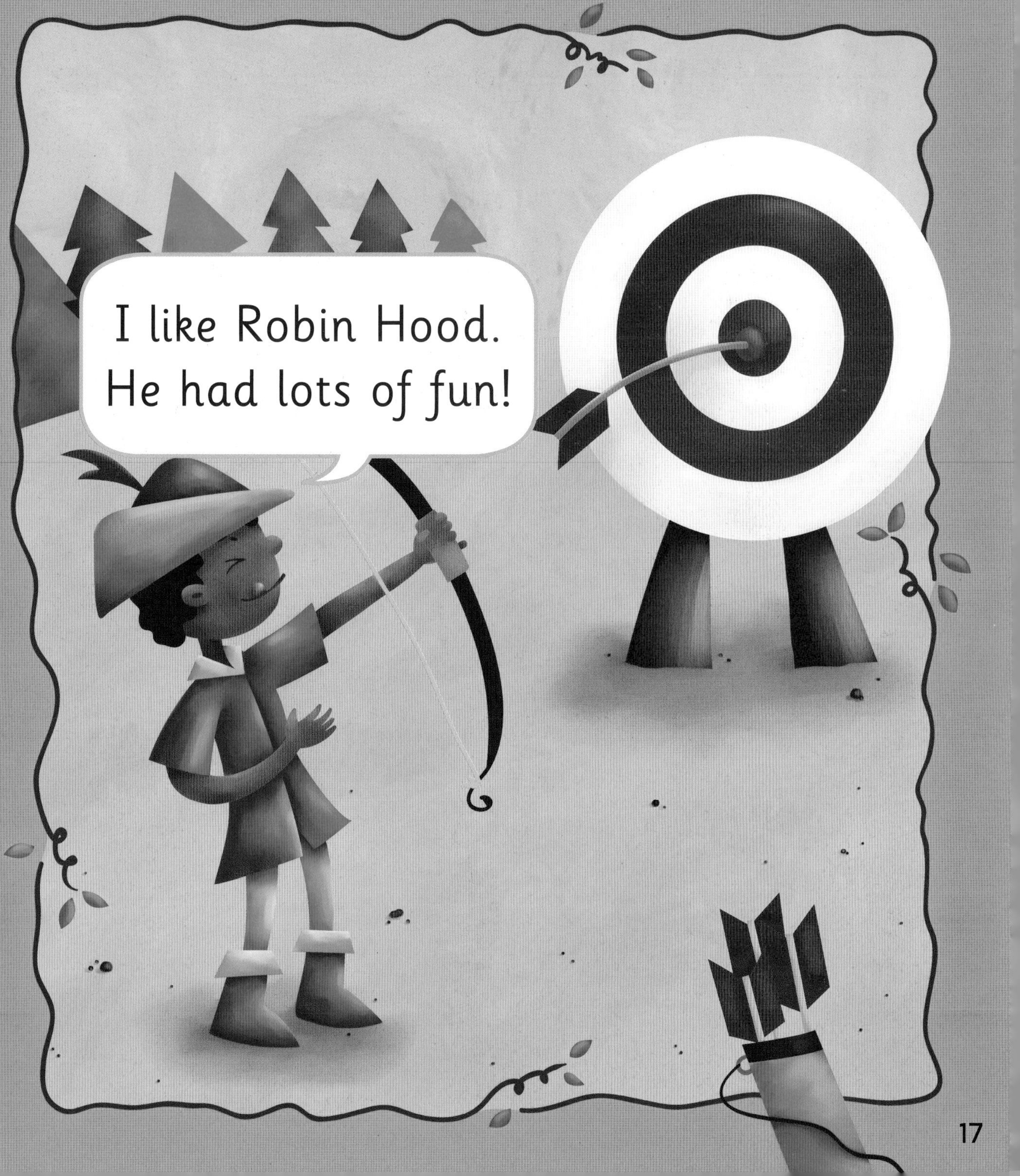
I like Robin Hood.
He had lots of fun!

Mum did not know which outfit to buy. Jed took Mum to the toyshop next door.

Mum sat down and thought about the dresses.

Jed played with the racing car.

Dad got home from work.
He had on his work uniform.
It gave mum an idea.

It was the night of the party.
Dad was ready to go. Mum was upstairs.

Gran, Jed and Dad waited for Mum.
She took a very look time.

At last, Mum was ready for the party.

My party dress is your work uniform!

We like it!

Story Words

cowboy

Dad

dress

footballer

garage

Gran

Mum

pirate

racing car driver

Robin Hood

shopkeeper

shops

uniform

Let's Talk About The Party Dress

Look carefully at the book cover.

What dressing up costumes can you see?

This is a bright, bold front cover. Can you name all the colours?

Jed wants to have lots of different jobs when he grows up.

What do you want to be when you're older?

Would you need to wear a uniform? Can you describe it?

The story is all about different kinds of clothes.

What do you like to wear?

Do you like to dress up and pretend to be different people? Maybe you like being an astronaut or a scientist!

Jed's mum recycles some of Dad's work clothes into a new outfit.

Have you ever made something new out of something old?

What other items do you recycle at home?

Did you like the ending of the story?

Give reasons for your answer.

What did you think of Mum's new outfit?

Fun and Games

The story is about dressing up and the sorts of clothes people wear to do different jobs. Read the job words below. Can you match them to the correct pictures?

shopkeeper   footballer   pirate   racing car driver

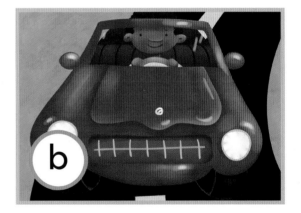

Complete these story sentences by filling in the gaps with the words below.

garage   Robin Hood   party   uniform

1. Dad got home from work. He had on his work ....

2. Jed's mum and dad had been invited to a ....

3. "I could dress up as .... !"

4. Dad worked at the car ....

Your Turn

Now that you have read the story,
have a go at telling it in your own words.
Use the pictures below to help you.

GET TO KNOW READING GEMS

Reading Gems is a series of books that has been written for children who are learning to read. The books have been created in consultation with a literacy specialist.

The books fit into four levels, with each level getting more challenging as a child's confidence and reading ability grows. The simple text and fun illustrations provide gradual, structured practice of reading. Most importantly, these books are good stories that are fun to read!

Level 1 is for children who are taking their first steps into reading. Story themes and subjects are familiar to young children, and there is lots of repetition to build reading confidence.

Level 2 is for children who have taken their first reading steps and are becoming readers. Story themes are still familiar but sentences are a bit longer, as children begin to tackle more challenging vocabulary.

Level 3 is for children who are developing as readers. Stories and subjects are varied, and more descriptive words are introduced.

Level 4 is for readers who are rapidly growing in reading confidence and independence. There is less repetition on the page, broader themes are explored and plot lines straddle multiple pages.

The Party Dress is all about dresing up and pretending. It looks at themes of imagination and play, as well as recycling.

Level 3